Rock 'n' Roll Classics
for Keyboard

Music arranged and processed by Barnes Music Engraving Ltd.,
East Sussex TN22 4HA, UK.

Published 1994

International MUSIC Publications

International Music Publications Limited
Griffin House 161 Hammersmith Road London W6 8BS England

ALL SHOOK UP

Words & Music by Otis Blackwell and Elvis Presley

Suggested Registration: Saxophone
Rhythm: Shuffle
Tempo: ♩ = 132

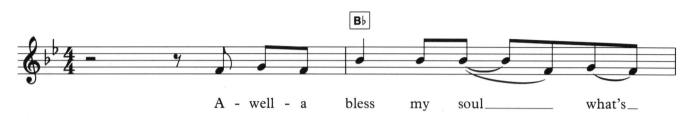

A - well - a bless my soul _____ what's _

wrong with me? _ I'm itch-ing like a man _ on a fuz - zy tree. _

My friends say _ I'm act-in' queer as a bug, _ I'm in love, I'm

all shook up, _ u-huh - huh, oh yeah, _ yeah.

Please don't ask what's on my mind, I'm a lit - tle mixed up but I'm

feel - ing fine. _ When I'm near that girl that I love the best, _ my

heart beats so it scares me to death. She touched my hand, what a

chill I got,___ her kis - ses are like___ a vol -

- ca - no, that's hot.___ I'm proud to say she's my

but - ter - cup,__ I'm in love, I'm all shook up,__ u - huh -

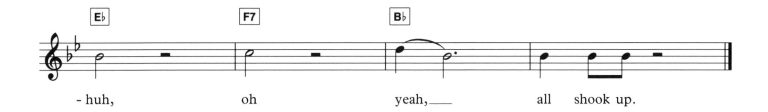

- huh, oh yeah,___ all shook up.

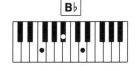
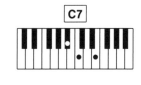
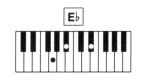
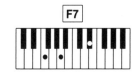

AT THE HOP

Words & Music by John Medora, David White and Arthur Singer

Suggested Registration: Electric Guitar
Rhythm: Rock & Roll / 8 Beat
Tempo: ♩ = 164

Ah   ah   ah   ah,   ah   ah   ah   ah,

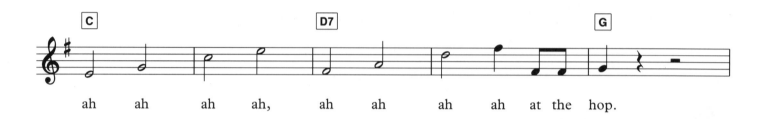

ah   ah   ah   ah,   ah   ah   ah   ah   at the hop.

Well   you   can   rock   it,   you   can   roll   it,   do   the

stomp   and   ev - en   stroll   it,   at   the   hop.

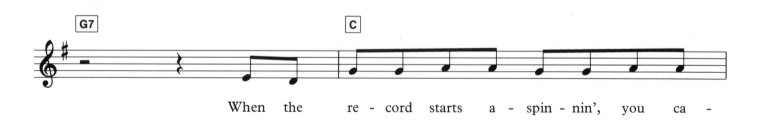

When   the   re - cord   starts   a - spin - nin',   you   ca -

- lyp - so   when   you   chic - ken,   at   the   hop.

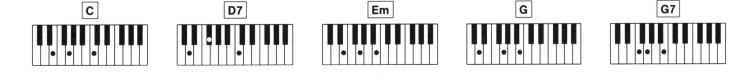

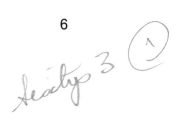

Be-Bop-A-Lula

Words & Music by Gene Vincent and Sheriff Tex Davis

Suggested Registration: Jazz Organ
Rhythm: Shuffle
Tempo: ♩ = 100

She's the girl in the red blue jeans,

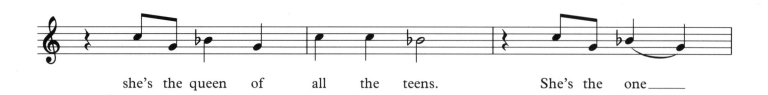

she's the queen of all the teens. She's the one____

that I know, she's the one that loves me so.

Be-bop-a-lu-la, she's my ba-by, Be-bop-a-lu-la, I

don't mean may-be. Be-bop-a-lu-la, she's my ba-by

love, my ba-by love, my ba-by love. She's the one that's

got that beat, she's the one with the fly - in' feet.

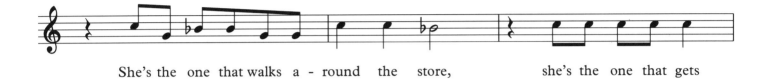

She's the one that walks a - round the store, she's the one that gets

F7

more and more. Be - bop - a - lu - la, she's my ba - by,

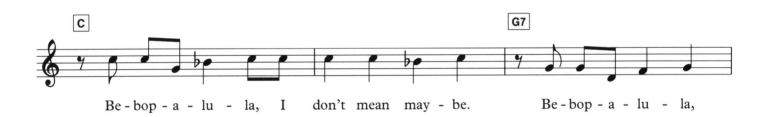

C   **G7**

Be - bop - a - lu - la, I don't mean may - be. Be - bop - a - lu - la,

C

she's my ba - by love, my ba - by love, my ba - by love.

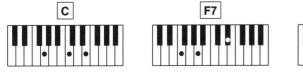

C   **F7**

G7

BLUE SUEDE SHOES

Words & Music by Carl Lee Perkins

Suggested Registration: Jazz Guitar
Rhythm: Shuffle
Tempo: ♩ = 150

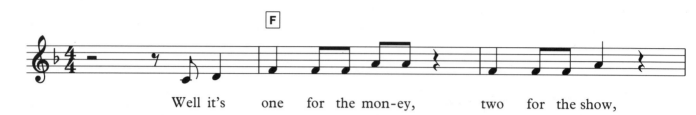

Well it's one for the mon-ey, two for the show,

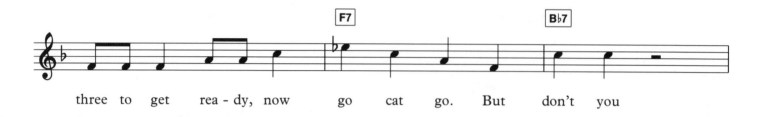

three to get rea-dy, now go cat go. But don't you

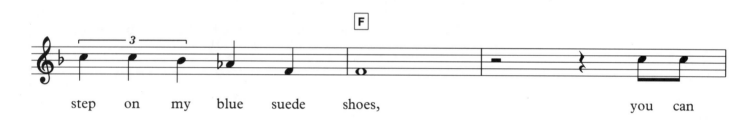

step on my blue suede shoes, you can

do a-ny-thing,_ but lay off-a my blue suede shoes._

Well you can knock me down, step in my face,_

slan-der my name all ov-er the place. Do a-ny-thing_ that you

want to do,___ but uh – uh hon-ey lay off - a my shoes.

Don't you step on my blue suede shoes,

you can do a - ny - thing, but lay off - a my blue suede

shoes, you can do a - ny - thing,___ but lay

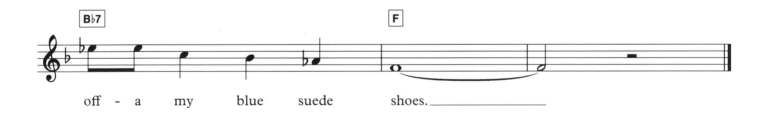

off - a my blue suede shoes.___

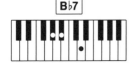
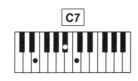
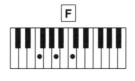
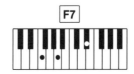

BOOK OF LOVE

Words & Music by Charles Patrick, Warren Davis and George Malone

Suggested Registration: Piano
Rhythm: 8 Beat
Tempo: ♩ = 150

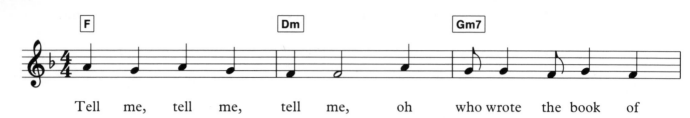

Tell me, tell me, tell me, oh who wrote the book of

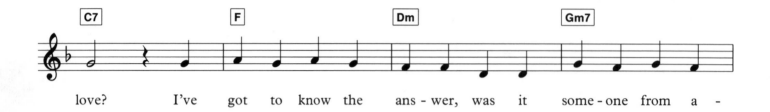

love? I've got to know the ans-wer, was it some-one from a-

- bove? I won-der, won-der who,_____

who, who wrote the book of love?_____

Chap-ter one says to love her, to love her with all your

heart, chap-ter two you tell her you're

© 1957 & 1994 Arc Music Corp, USA
Tristan Music Ltd, London WC2H 8NA

ne - ver, ne - ver, ne - ver, ne - ver ev - er gon - na part. In chap - ter three re -

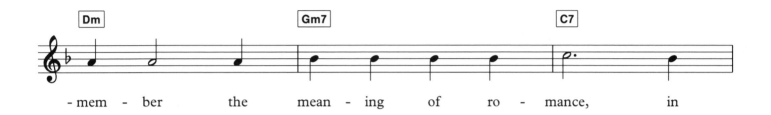

- mem - ber the mean - ing of ro - mance, in

chap - ter four you break up, but you give her just one more

chance. Oh I won - der, won - der who,_____

who, who wrote the book of love?_____

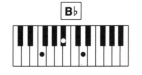

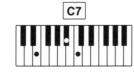

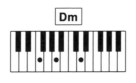

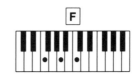

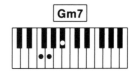

C'MON EVERYBODY

Words & Music by Eddie Cochran and Jerry Capehart

Suggested Registration: Electric Guitar
Rhythm: 8 Beat
Tempo: ♩ = 150

Well c' - mon ev-ery-bo-dy and let's get to-ge-ther to-night. __

I got some mon-ey in my jeans and I'm real-ly gon-na spend it right. __

Been a - do - in' my home - work all week long, now the

house is emp-ty, the folks are gone. C' - mon ev-ery-bo - dy!

Well my

ba - by's num-ber one, but I'm gon - na dance with three or four. __

And the house-'ll be shak-ing from my bare feet slap-pin' the floor.

— When you hear that mu-sic your feet won't sit still, if your

bro - ther won't, then your sis - ter will. C' -

- mon ev - ery - bo - dy!

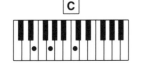

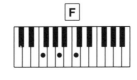

Great Balls Of Fire

Words & Music by Jack Hammer and Otis Blackwell

Suggested Registration: Saxophone
Rhythm: Rock / Rock & Roll
Tempo: ♩ = 140

You shake my nerves and you rat - tle my brain, _

too much love drives a man in - sane, _ you broke my will,

but what a thrill, good - ness gra - cious, great _ balls of fi - re.

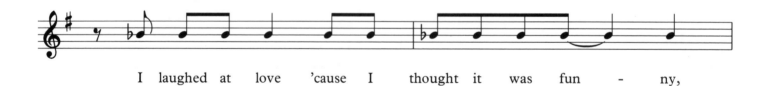

I laughed at love 'cause I thought it was fun - ny,

you came a - long and moved _ me hon - ey, I changed my mind,

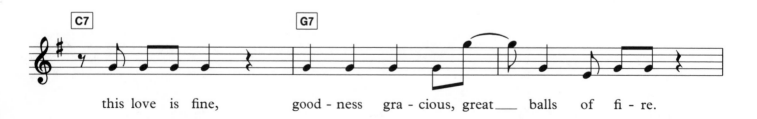

this love is fine, good - ness gra - cious, great _ balls of fi - re.

Kiss me ba - by, oh yo, it feels good, hold me ba - by, I want to love you like a lov - er should, you're fine, __ so kind, __ I'm gon-na tell the world that you're mine, mine, mine, mine. I chew my nails and I twid-dle my thumbs, I'm real ner-vous, but it sure is fun, __ oh ba - by, you're driv-ing me cra - zy, good - ness gra - cious, great __ balls of fi - re.

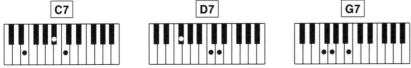

Sixty 3 Birc free (1)

HEARTBREAK HOTEL

Words & Music by Mae Boren Axton, Tommy Durden and Elvis Presley

Suggested Registration: Saxophone
Rhythm: Shuffle
Tempo: ♩. = 68

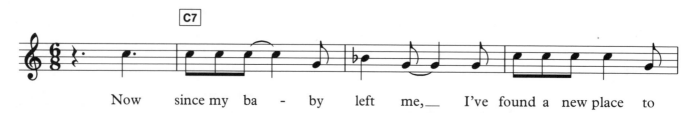

Now since my ba - by left me, ___ I've found a new place to

dwell, down at the end of Lone - ly Street at Heart-break Ho - tel. ___

I feel so lone - ly, I feel so lone - ly,

I feel so lone - ly ___ I could die.

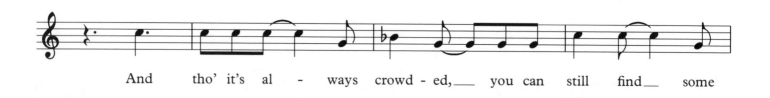

And tho' it's al - ways crowd - ed, ___ you can still find ___ some

room, for bro - ken heart - ed lov - ers to cry there in the

HOUND DOG

Words & Music by Jerry Leiber and Mike Stoller

Suggested Registration: Saxophone
Rhythm: Rock Ballad
Tempo: ♩ = 166

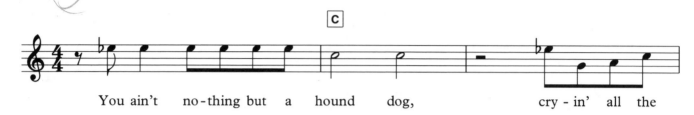

You ain't no-thing but a hound dog, cry - in' all the

time. You ain't no - thing but a hound dog,

cry - in' all the time. Well___ you ain't

ne - ver caught a rab - bit, and you ain't no friend of mine.

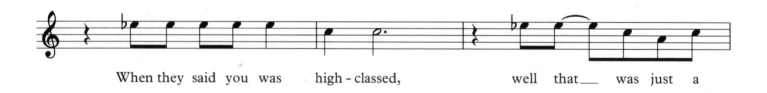

When they said you was high - classed, well that___ was just a

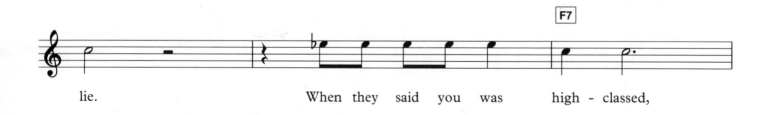

lie. When they said you was high - classed,

well that___ was just a lie.   Well___ you ain't

ne - ver caught a rab - bit, and you ain't no friend of mine.

You ain't no - thin' but a hound dog,   cry - in' all the

time.   You ain't no - thin' but a hound dog,

cry - in' all the time.   Well___ you ain't

ne - ver caught a rab-bit, and you ain't no friend of mine.

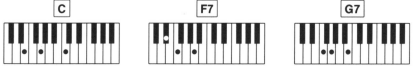

I Hear You Knocking

Words & Music by Dave Bartholomew and Pearl King

Suggested Registration: Electric Guitar
Rhythm: 8 Beat
Tempo: ♩ = 132

You went a - way and left me long time a - go,___ and

now you're knock - ing on my door.___ I hear you

knock - ing, but you can't___ come in,

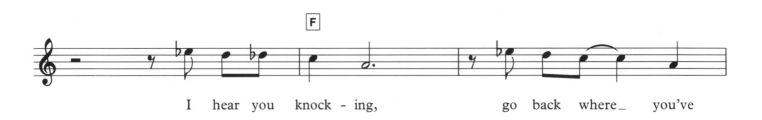

I hear you knock - ing, go back where_ you've

been. I begged you not to go but you

said good-bye,__ and now you tell me all your lies.__ I hear you

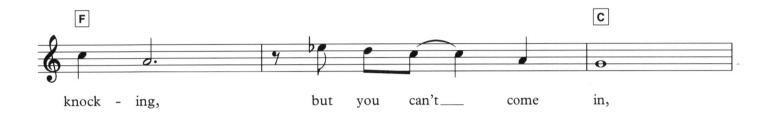

knock - ing, but you can't__ come in,

I hear you knock - ing, go back where_ you've

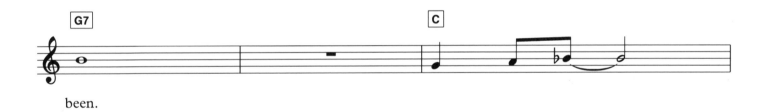

been.

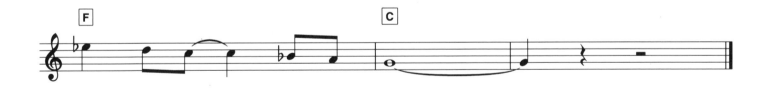

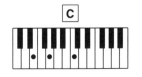
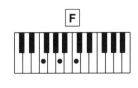
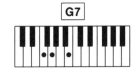

Jailhouse Rock

Words & Music by Jerry Leiber and Mike Stoller

Suggested Registration: Saxophone
Rhythm: Shuffle
Tempo: ♩ = 160

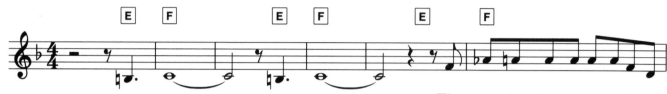

The war-den threw a par-ty in the

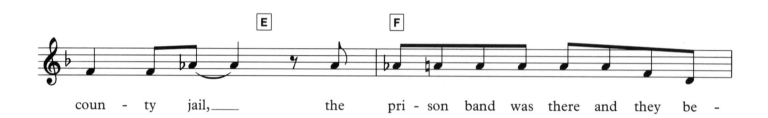

coun-ty jail,___ the pri-son band was there and they be -

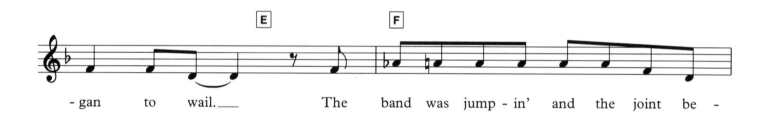

-gan to wail.___ The band was jump-in' and the joint be -

-gan to swing,___ you should have heard those knocked out

jail - birds sing. Let's rock, let's rock,

ev - ery - bo - dy in the whole cell block was danc -

Carlin Music Corp, London NW1 8BD

Johnny B Goode

Words & Music by Chuck Berry

Suggested Registration: Electric Guitar
Rhythm: 8 Beat
Tempo: ♩ = 140

Deep down in Lou-'si-an-a close to New Or-leans, 'way

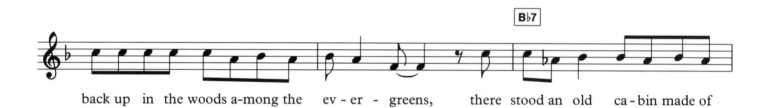

back up in the woods a-mong the ev-er-greens, there stood an old ca-bin made of

earth and wood, where lived a coun-try boy named John-ny B Goode, who'd

ne-ver ev-er learned to read or write so well,___ but he could

play a gui-tar___ just like a-ring-ing a bell.__ He used to car-ry his gui-tar in a

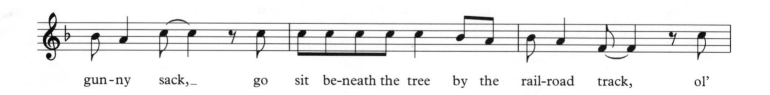

gun-ny sack,_ go sit be-neath the tree by the rail-road track, ol'

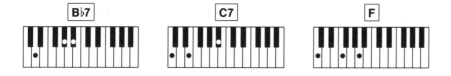

Peggy Sue

Words & Music by Jerry Allison, Norman Petty and Buddy Holly

Suggested Registration: Trumpet
Rhythm: 8 Beat
Tempo: ♩ = 140

If you knew_ Peg - gy Sue,_ then you'd know why

I feel blue, a-bout Peg - gy, 'bout my Peg - gy Sue._____

Oh well I love you gal,_ yes I love you Peg - gy Sue._

_ Peg - gy Sue,_ Peg - gy Sue,_

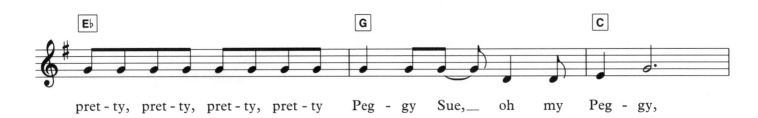

pret - ty, pret - ty, pret - ty, pret - ty Peg - gy Sue,_ oh my Peg - gy,

my Peg - gy Sue._____ Oh well I

love you gal,__ and I need you Peg - gy Sue.__

I love you__ Peg - gy Sue,__ with a love so

rare and true,__ oh Peg - gy, my Peg - gy Sue.__

_____ Oh well I love you gal,__ and I

want you Peg - gy Sue._____

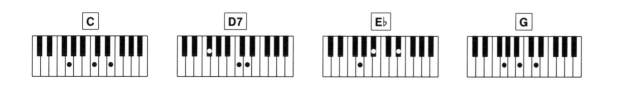

Reet Petite
(The Sweetest Girl In Town)

Words & Music by Tyran Carlo and Berry Gordy Jr

Suggested Registration: Jazz Organ
Rhythm: Shuffle
Tempo: ♩ = 146

Well

look a-bout, look a-bout, look a-bout, look a-bout ooh_____ wee._

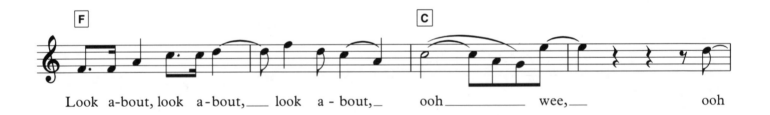

Look a-bout, look a-bout,_ look a - bout,_ ooh_____ wee,_ ooh

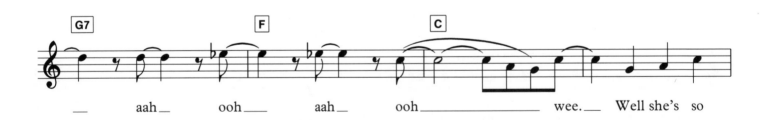

_ aah_ ooh_ aah_ ooh_____ wee._ Well she's so

fine, fine, fine,___ she's so fine, f - f - fine,___ she's so

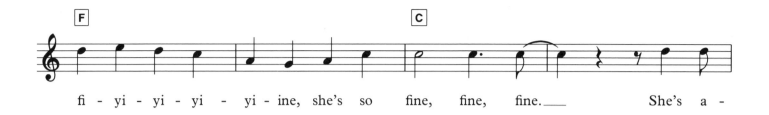

fi - yi - yi - yi - yi - ine, she's so fine, fine, fine.___ She's a -

-real-ly sweet, the fin-est girl you ev - er want to meet. Oh oh oh

oh, oh_ oh oh oh oh. Oh

Reet Pe - tite__ the fin-est girl you ev - er want to meet, oh

Reet Pe - tite__ the fin-est girl you ev - er want to meet.

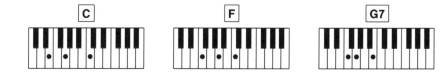

Rock Around The Clock

Words & Music by Max C Freedman and Jimmy Daknight

Suggested Registration: Saxophone
Rhythm: Shuffle
Tempo: ♩ = 160

One two three o'-clock four o'-clock rock, five six seven o'-clock

eight o'-clock rock, nine ten e-leven o'-clock twelve o'-clock rock, we're gon-na

rock a-round the clock to-night. Put your glad rags on and

join me hon',_ we'll have some fun when the clock strikes one, we're gon-na

rock a-round the clock to-night,_ we're gon-na

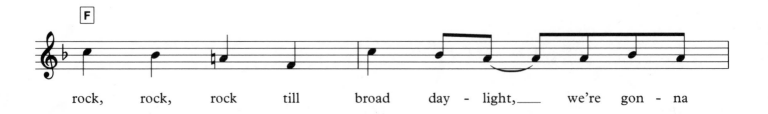

rock, rock, rock till broad day-light,_ we're gon-na

ROLL OVER, BEETHOVEN

Words & Music by Chuck Berry

Suggested Registration: Piano
Rhythm: Rock / 8 Beat
Tempo: ♩ = 140

Well I'm a - write a lit - tle let - ter, gon - na mail it to my lo - cal D. J.___

___ Yes it's a jump - in' lit - tle re - cord I

want my joc - key to play.___ Roll ov -

- er Beet - ho - ven, I got - ta hear it a - gain to - day,___

you know my temp - 'ra - ture's ris - in' and the juke box blow - in' a

fuse. My heart's beat - in' rhy - thm and my

SHAKE, RATTLE AND ROLL

Words & Music by Charles Calhoun

Suggested Registration: Saxophone
Rhythm: Shuffle
Tempo: ♩ = 140

Get out from that kit-chen and rat-tle those pots and

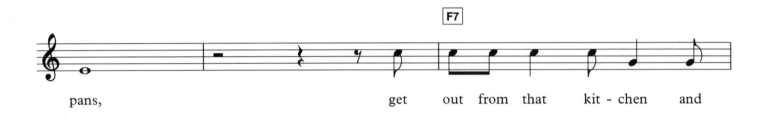

pans, get out from that kit-chen and

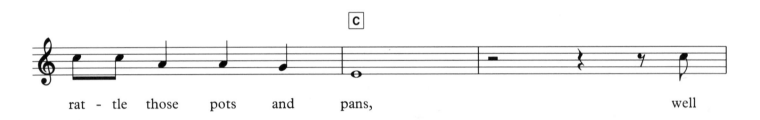

rat-tle those pots and pans, well

roll my break-fast, 'cause I'm a hun - gry man.

Wear-ing those dres-ses your hair done up so right,

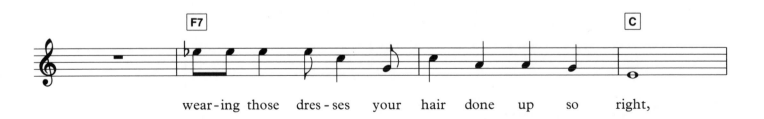

wear-ing those dres-ses your hair done up so right,

you look so warm but your heart is cold____ as ice.

Shake, rat - tle and roll,____ I said

shake, rat - tle and roll,____ I said shake, rat - tle and roll,__

__ I said shake, rat - tle and roll.____ You

ne - ver do no - thin' to save your dog - gone soul.

Shake, rat - tle and roll._____

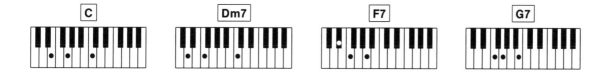

Summertime Blues

Words & Music by Eddie Cochran and Jerry Capehart

Suggested Registration: Electric Guitar
Rhythm: 8 Beat
Tempo: ♩ = 140

I'm a - gon-na raise a fuss, I'm a - gon-na raise a hol - ler, a-bout a - work-in' all sum-mer just to try to earn a dol - lar. Ev - ery time I call my ba-by, try to get a date, my boss says 'No dice son you got - ta work late.'__ Some-times I won-der what I'm a-gon-na do,__ but there ain't no cure for the sum-mer - time__ blues. I'm gon-na take two weeks, gon-na have a fine va - ca - tion.

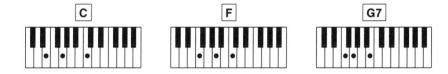

THREE STEPS TO HEAVEN

Words & Music by Bob Cochran and Eddie Cochran

Suggested Registration: Piano
Rhythm: Slow Latin
Tempo: ♩ = 134

Now there are three _____ steps to

Hea - ven, _____ just lis - ten and

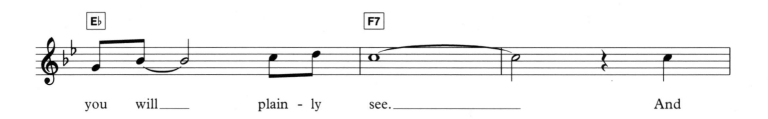

you will ___ plain - ly see. _____ And

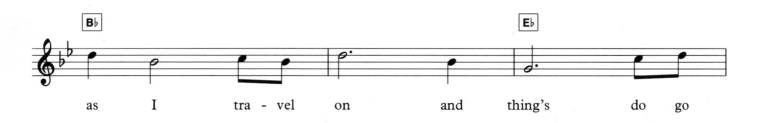

as I tra - vel on and thing's do go

wrong, just call it steps one, two and

three. _____ Step one, _____ you

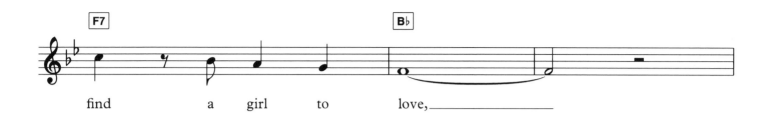

find   a   girl   to   love,_____

step   two,_____   she   falls   in   love   with   you._____

_____   Step   three_____ you   kiss   and   hold   her

tight - ly,_____   well   that   sure   seems   like

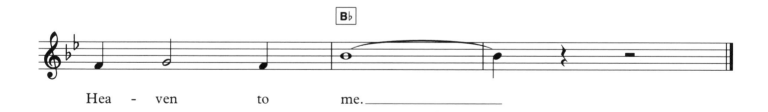

Hea - ven   to   me._____

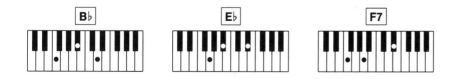

TUTTI FRUTTI

Words & Music by R Penniman and D La Bostrie

Suggested Registration: Saxophone
Rhythm: Shuffle
Tempo: ♩ = 162

A - bop - bop a - loom-op a - lop - bop boom. Tut - ti

Frut - ti, au rut - ti. Tut - ti Frut - ti, au

rut - ti. Tut - ti Frut - ti, au rut - ti. Tut - ti

Frut - ti, au rut - ti. Tut - ti Frut - ti, au

rut - ti. A - bop - bop a - loom-op a - lop - bop boom. I got a

gal her name's Sue, she knows just what to do,___

WAKE UP LITTLE SUZIE

Words & Music by Boudleaux Bryant and Felice Bryant

Suggested Registration: Piano
Rhythm: 8 Beat
Tempo: ♩ = 164

Wake up   lit - tle   Su -   zie,

wake up.   Wake up   lit - tle

Su -   zie,   wake up.   We've

both been sound a - sleep,   wake up lit - tle Su - zie and

weep.   The   mo - vie's   ov - er, it's   four   o' - clock and

we're   in   trou - ble deep. Wake up___ lit - tle Su - zie,___

wake up___ lit - tle Su - zie.___ Well

what we gon - na tell you ma - ma?___ What we gon - na tell your

pa? What we gon - na tell our friends, when they say

'Ooh la la.' Wake up lit - tle Su - zie,___

wake up___ lit - tle Su - zie.___

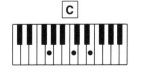
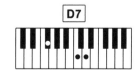
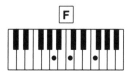
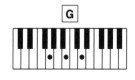
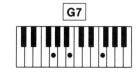

WHOLE LOT-TA SHAKIN' GOIN' ON

Words & Music by Dave Williams and Sunny David

Suggested Registration: Electric Guitar
Rhythm: Shuffle
Tempo: ♩ = 160

Come on ov - er ba - by,____

whole lot - ta sha - kin' goin' on.____ Come on ov - er ba -

- by,____ an' ba - by you can't go wrong.____

Ain't no - bo - dy fak - in',____ whole lot - ta shak - in' goin' on.____

EMI Music Publishing Ltd, London WC2H 0EA

Wooden Heart

Words & Music by Fred Wise, Ben Weisman, Kay Twomey and Bert Kaempfert

Suggested Registration: Piano
Rhythm: Shuffle
Tempo: ♩ = 138

Can't you see I love you, please don't

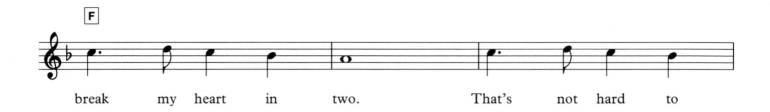

break my heart in two. That's not hard to

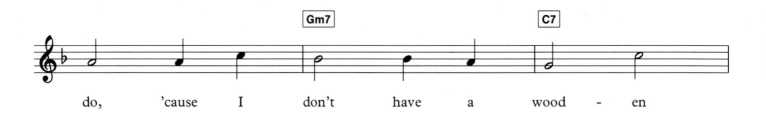

do, 'cause I don't have a wood - en

heart._____ And if you say 'Good -

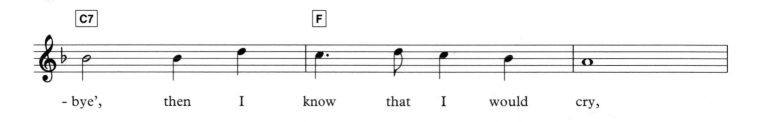

- bye', then I know that I would cry,

may - be I would die, 'cause I don't have a

wood - en heart._____ There's no

strings up - on this love of mine, it was

al - ways you from the start,_____ treat me

nice, treat me good, treat me like you real - ly

should, 'cause I'm not made of wood, and I

don't have a wood - en heart._____

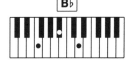
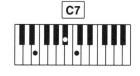
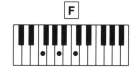
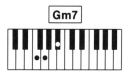

Printed and bound in Great Britain

The Easy Keyboard Library Series

Big Band Hits Order Ref: 19098	**Popular Classics** Order Ref: 4180A
Blues Order Ref: 3477A	**Pub Singalong Collection** Order Ref: 3954A
Celebration Songs Order Ref: 3478A	**Rock 'n' Roll Classics** Order Ref: 2224A
Christmas Carols Order Ref: 4616A	**Traditional Scottish Favourites** Order Ref: 4231A
Christmas Songs Order Ref: 19198	**Showtunes - Volume 1** Order Ref: 19103
Classic Hits - Volume 1 Order Ref: 19099	**Showtunes - Volume 2** Order Ref: 3328A
Classic Hits - Volume 2 Order Ref: 19100	**Soft Rock Collection** Order Ref: 4617A
Country Songs Order Ref: 19101	**Soul Classics** Order Ref: 19201
Traditional English Favourites Order Ref: 4229A	**Summer Collection** Order Ref: 3489A
Favourite Hymns Order Ref: 4179A	**TV Themes** Order Ref: 19196
Film Classics Order Ref: 19197	**The Twenties** Order Ref: 2969A
Great Songwriters Order Ref: 2225A	**The Thirties** Order Ref: 2970A
Instrumental Classics Order Ref: 2338A	**The Forties** Order Ref: 2971A
Traditional Irish Favourites Order Ref: 4230A	**The Fifties** Order Ref: 2972A
Love Songs - Volume 1 Order Ref: 19102	**The Sixties** Order Ref: 2973A
Love Songs - Volume 2 Order Ref: 19199	**The Seventies** Order Ref: 2974A
Music Hall Order Ref: 3329A	**The Eighties** Order Ref: 2975A
Motown Classics Order Ref: 2337A	**The Nineties** Order Ref: 2976A
Number One Hits Order Ref: 19200	**Wartime Collection** Order Ref: 3955A

Wedding Collection
Order Ref: 3688A

Exclusive distributors:

International Music Publications Limited
Griffin House 161 Hammersmith Road London W6 8BS, England
International Music Publications Limited
25 Rue D'Hauteville, 75010 Paris, France
International Music Publications GmbH Germany
Marstallstrasse 8, D-80539 München, Germany
Nuova Carisch S.R.L.
Via M.F. Quintiliano 40, 20138 Milano, Italy
Danmusik
Vognmagergade 7, DK-1120 Copenhagen K, Denmark